Field Guide to the Submerged Aquatic Vegetation of Chesapeake Bay

by

Linda M. Hurley
U.S. Fish and Wildlife Service
Chesapeake Bay Estuary Program
Annapolis, Maryland

Table of Contents

Preface

The *Field Guide to the Submerged Aquatic Vegetation of Chesapeake Bay* was developed to aid in the identification of these important underwater plants. Although the different species can sometimes be found in botanical publications dealing with aquatic vegetation, they are usually presented along with emergent marsh plants, floating-leaved plants and algae. A few publications exist that emphasize the submerged plants, but they tend to be regional in scope and do not focus on all species found in the Chesapeake Bay and its tidal tributaries.

This field guide covers the underwater vascular plants known as submerged aquatic vegetation (SAV) or, as they are referred to locally, "bay grasses". A few non-SAV species are described in the field guide only to avoid their confusion with true SAV. This publication is distinct from other aquatic plant publications because it includes color photographs as well as line drawings and descriptive text to more accurately distinguish the individual species.

SAV is an important part of the Chesapeake Bay ecosystem. Protection and enhancement of SAV will help to preserve this delicately balanced estuarine system with its wealth of natural resources. The field guide is intended as a tool for natural resource managers and biologists involved with SAV protection and research. It is also designed as an educational aid for students, amateur naturalists, and the general public interested in Chesapeake Bay ecology.

Acknowledgments

Special thanks are extended to Steven Ailstock, Anne Arundel Community College; G. Michael Haramis, U.S. Fish and Wildlife Service; Tom Nebel, U.S. Fish and Wildlife Service and Henry M. Snyder, U.S. Park Service for their assistance.

I would particularly like to thank Henry G. Dunn, Visual Information Manager of the Baltimore District Corps of Engineers for his masterful coordination, design and production management of this publication.

Also, appreciation is extended to members of the U.S. Fish and Wildlife Service's Chesapeake Bay Estuary Program and the Annapolis Field Office for their assistance in SAV field collections. Their "helping hands" actually appear in many of the photos.

Introduction

Types of Aquatic Vegetation

Many different forms of aquatic vegetation exist, ranging from the tiny algae or phytoplankton that float in the waters of the world to the bald cypress trees of inland freshwater swamps. Within this realm of aquatic vegetation is a smaller collection of individuals known as aquatic vascular plants.

The botanical method of presenting these various plants is to describe them by their taxonomic grouping into the appropriate plant family, genus and species. However, another method might be to separate the plants into different groups based upon their growth and habitat characteristics. Using this approach, one could divide these plants into three basic types: submerged aquatic vegetation (SAV), floating aquatic vegetation (FAV), and emergent aquatic vegetation (EAV).

The focus of this field guide is on SAV found in the Chesapeake Bay. However, all three aquatic plant types can be found growing within the same location and identification may be difficult. For this reason, some basic definitions of these plant groups are given.

Submerged Aquatic Vegetation—SAV

SAV refers to those vascular plants that live and grow completely underwater or just up to the water surface. A few species, when in flower, may have their flowers protruding just above the

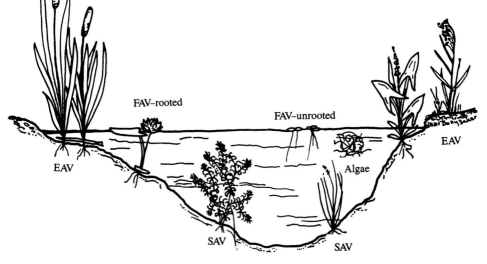

FAV–rooted

FAV–unrooted

EAV

EAV

Algae

SAV

SAV

water surface. However, at all other times SAV is found growing entirely submerged. In fact, when removed from water for any extended length of time, SAV will become desiccated and die.

The roots, stems and leaves of SAV contain the conducting tissues characteristic of all true vascular plants. But because SAV is aquatic, they have special adaptations to this type of environment. For example, the stems and leaves of SAV lack plant tissues for structural support because the surrounding water provides that support. The leaves and stems also contain specialized cells called "aerenchyma" which are thin-walled cells with large intercellular air spaces. These serve to provide additional buoyancy and support to the plants.

The leaves and stems are generally thin and lack the waxy covering on their surfaces called the "cuticle" that is characteristic of most terrestrial plants. This increases the exchange of water, nutrients and gasses between the plant and the surrounding aquatic medium. This is why SAV rapidly loses its moisture when removed from the water. Examples of SAV include sago pondweed *(Potamogeton pectinatus)*, redhead grass *(Potamogeton perfoliatus)* and eelgrass *(Zostera marina)*.

Floating Aquatic Vegetation—FAV

Floating aquatic vegetation refers to those plants with their leaves floating on top of the water surface. These plants may or may not be anchored to the substrate by underwater stems and roots. Like SAV, these plants rely on water for their support and have reduced tissues for mechanical support. The stems and leaves have tiny air spaces in the tissues that provide buoyancy for floatation.

The floating leaves are simultaneously exposed to air and water. The lower surface of FAV leaves usually lacks a cuticle while the upper leaf surfaces tend to have waxy cuticles. This allows the underside of the leaves to exchange water and nutrients with the aquatic environment while the upper leaf surface is protected from excessive evaporation of water from the plant to the air. The upper, waxy cuticle also tends to shed water, keeping the leaf from retaining water and becoming submersed. Examples of FAV include water lilies *(Nymphaea* spp.), American lotus *(Nelumbo lutea)*, and duckweed *(Lemna* spp.).

Emergent Aquatic Vegetation—EAV

These plants have their upper stems and leaves protruding above and out of the water while the lower stems and roots are below the water surface. EAV may sometimes be found completely under the water surface, especially during their early growth stages, during

General Ecology

high tides and flooding. Typically, however, the leaves of EAV extend out of the water and are exposed to the air.

Emergent plants tend to have rigid stems and leaves to support the aerial portions of the plant. The leaves of EAV are much the same as terrestrial plant leaves. They are covered on the upper and lower surface by the layer of cuticle which retards the evaporation of water from the plant. The upper layer, generally exposed more to the sun, tends to be thicker than the lower layer. Examples of EAV include salt-marsh cordgrass *(Spartina alterniflora)*, cattail (*Typha* spp.), and arrowhead (*Sagittaria* spp.).

Algae

Although they are not vascular plants, certain forms of algae are sometimes confused with SAV. Algae do not have the specialized plant cells or tissues for transporting water and nutrients as do true vascular plants with their root-stem-leaf system.

Algae can occur as tiny single-celled free-floating plants referred to as phytoplankton, or they can occur as multicellular units forming filamentous chains or colonies. These may appear as slimy, green mats or clumps covering rocks or pilings. Larger algae, often called seaweeds, are sometimes misidentified as SAV. Examples described in more detail in a later section include muskgrass (*Chara* spp.) and sea lettuce *(Ulva lactuca).*

Species

Worldwide, there are well over 500 species of submerged aquatic vegetation ranging from those that inhabit freshwater and brackish environments to those found in the high salinity waters of the world's oceans. In the Chesapeake Bay and its tidal tributaries, 15 species representing nine plant families commonly occur. A few of these are not native to the United States but have become established in recent years and now can be found in many areas around the Bay. This field guide covers the dominant SAV species and includes a few species of algae and floating aquatic plants because of their similarity of appearance to SAV.

Habitat Requirements

SAV are found in shallow areas where sufficient light for photosynthesis can penetrate through the water. In the Chesapeake Bay region this is normally in water less than six feet deep. Some species of SAV can tolerate low light levels and are better able to exist under more turbid conditions and in deeper waters.

Different species of SAV have different salinity requirements and in Chesapeake Bay, salinity is a primary factor influencing their distribution.

The Chesapeake Bay with its many tributaries provides a full range of salinity environments. The upper portions of rivers that flow into the Bay consist mostly of freshwater while the middle and lower portions have higher salinities.

4

CHESAPEAKE BAY SALINITY

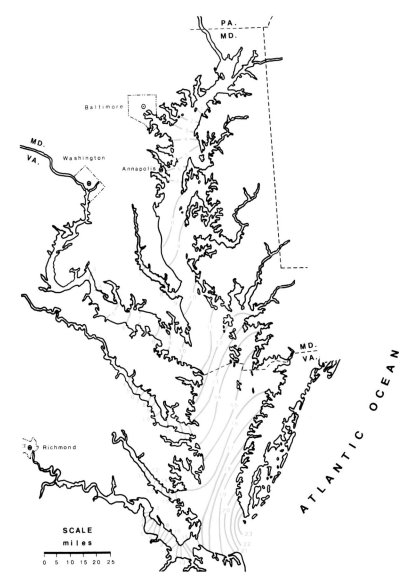

SPRING

In the Chesapeake Bay there are areas of equal salinity called isohalines. These lines tilt upwards toward the east because salty water flowing up the Bay and fresher water flowing down the Bay move toward the right due to the rotation of the earth. The isohalines shown are for the spring months. In summer or autumn, or in dry years, the lines will be displaced north and west as much as 12 ppt.

Salinities in the northern portion of the Bay tend to be mainly fresh to brackish while the lower Bay has salinity reaching full strength seawater.

The seasons of the year also influence salinity distribution. The lowest salinities in the Bay generally occur in the spring when snowmelt and high rainfall occur. In contrast, following the drier summer months, autumn tends to have the highest salinities.

One commonly used system divides the Bay into four salinity zones: tidal fresh (0-0.5 ppt), slightly brackish or oligo-haline (0.5-5 ppt), moderately brackish or mesohaline (5-18 ppt), and high salinity or polyhaline (18-30 ppt). In this field guide, this system is used to define the salinity tolerances for each species.

Species such as wild celery (Vallisneria americana) and water stargrass (Heter-anthera dubia) are found in freshwater areas of the northern portion of the Bay, known as the Susquehanna Flats, and in the upper freshwater reaches of many rivers. In the more brackish waters of the middle Bay, such as around Eastern Bay near St. Michaels, redhead grass and Eurasian watermilfoil (Myriophyllum spicatum) routinely occur. In the lower Bay where salinities are the highest, species such as eelgrass and widgeon grass (Ruppia maritima) are predominant.

In addition to light and salinity require-ments, species differ in their needs for particular types of substrate. Some species such as redhead grass grow better on silt-mud bottoms, while eelgrass prefers a more sandy substrate.

Temperature is also important to SAV. For some species, water temperatures must reach a certain level before seed germination takes place. Higher tem-peratures may limit the growth of some species while others are not as adversely affected.

Water currents and wave action in-fluence species distribution. Species such as coontail (Ceratophyllum demer-sum), which lacks a root system, or common waterweed (Elodea canadensis), which is only weakly rooted to the sub-strate, are found in more protected, slow-moving waters. In contrast, sago pondweed has a dense root structure and can withstand stronger currents and wave energy.

Value of SAV

SAV performs a number of important ecological functions. It has long been recognized as a major source of food for waterfowl. Many parts of the plants such as the seeds and tubers and sometimes whole plants, are eaten by several species of ducks, geese and swans. The names of the SAV species often indicate the type of waterfowl that have a particular affinity for that species. For example, one of the favored foods of the redhead duck (Aythya americana) is redhead grass. Extensive beds of wild celery (Vallisneria americana) are known to attract canvasback ducks whose scientific name, Aythya valisineria, reflects this

food preference. In addition to waterfowl, small mammals, such as muskrats
and beavers, also consume SAV.

SAV plays the significant role of providing habitat and nursery areas for
many species of fish and invertebrates.
The beds of aquatic plants with their
numerous leaves and stems provide
cover for many small fish such as
minnows and killifish. Young spot
and juvenile striped bass seek refuge
from predators in the grass beds.
As Chesapeake Bay watermen are well
aware, molting blue crabs or "soft-
shells" can be found hiding in SAV
until their shells harden.

In addition to providing cover, fish and
shellfish find a diverse assemblage of
food sources within the plant beds. The
surfaces of the plant blades and stems
provide a substrate for the attachment
of algae, eggs, and many small invertebrates such as barnacles, sea squirts
and bryozoans. Still other organisms
live buried in the sediment among the
plant roots. These in turn, are grazed
upon by snails, worms, and other
animals as they move about the beds in
search of food.

When bay grasses die and decompose
they provide a source of detrital material.
This is further broken down as it is
used for food by many small invertebrates, tiny zooplankton and bacteria.
Thus SAV plays an important role in
the transfer of energy through the Bay
food chain.

Another valuable attribute of SAV is its

function of absorbing nutrients. Like all
plants, SAV needs certain amounts of
nutrients such as nitrogen and phosphorus
for growth and reproduction. However,
when these nutrients occur in excessive
amounts in the water they can stimulate
large, troublesome algal blooms. Following these blooms, the algae quickly
die and, upon decomposition, rapidly
deplete oxygen from the water which is
then detrimental to fish and other
organisms. SAV helps to remove some
of these nutrients from the water
column and, as part of the photosyn-
thetic process, SAV produces oxygen.
Also, when SAV dies it decomposes
much more slowly and therefore does
not cause such low oxygen levels
to occur.

SAV is important in the process of
removing suspended sediment from the
water. The leaves and stems reduce
water currents and wave energy while
the roots tend to bind the substrate.
This allows sediment suspended in the
water column to settle out and helps to
prevent bottom sediments from being
resuspended. SAV helps to retard shoreline erosion by absorbing wave energy.

Although SAV has numerous ecological
benefits, its commercial value is rather
limited. In the past, eelgrass had been
used for packing and upholstery stuff-
ing and also for insulation material. In
fact, during the early 1900s, a popular
housing insulation was made from eelgrass that became known as "Cabot's
Quilt" after its inventor, a descendent
of John Cabot. Because of its high sili-
con content, eelgrass is non-flammable

7

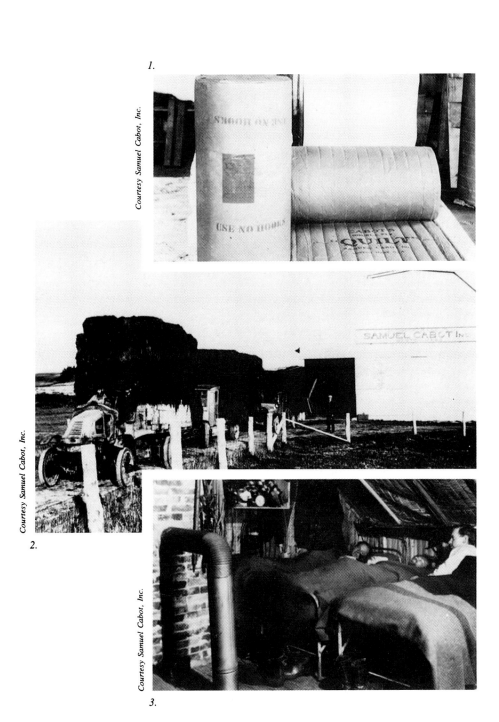

Courtesy Samuel Cabot, Inc.

1.

Courtesy Samuel Cabot, Inc.

2.

Courtesy Samuel Cabot, Inc.

3.

8

and when compressed and dried, it forms a loosely-matted framework with many air spaces giving it excellent insulation properties. Cabot's Quilt was used to line the walls of buildings at cold weather research stations. In addition to its warmth and fire resistent properties, the eelgrass quilt was useful as soundproofing material. Hotels, apartment buildings, and radio stations such as Radio City and Rockefeller Center of New York City were lined with these quilts. Today, synthetic products have replaced the use of these natural materials. Some Chesapeake Bay watermen however, still use eelgrass as packing material for live softshell crabs as they are shipped off to market.

Different species of SAV have been explored for use as livestock feed but their high water content (90-95%), low nutritional value, poor palatability and digestibility has made this infeasible. Use of SAV as mulching material is somewhat more practical, but limited because of difficulties with harvesting and transporting the material.

Distribution and Abundance

Populations of SAV undergo periods of fluctuation. During the early 1930s, eelgrass was afflicted with a mysterious "wasting disease" and practically disappeared from the coastal areas of the North Atlantic. However, by the 1940s, eelgrass seemed to be reestablishing into sizable beds.

Some exotic species that have made

Interstate Commission on the Potomac River Basin

4.

Vernon D. Stotts

5.

6.

their way into the United States have caused numerous problems due to their prolific growth capabilities. For example, during the 1940s water chestnut *(Trapa natans)*, a floating plant, so completely choked waterways in the Chesapeake Bay region that chemical and mechanical harvesting methods were used for its control. Eurasian watermilfoil temporarily displaced many native SAV species as it underwent a period of explosive growth throughout the Bay during the late 1950s and early 1960s. Boaters and fishermen complained of fouled boat propellers and fishing gear while others lost favorite swimming areas. Then, as quickly as milfoil infested the Bay, it naturally declined without any intervention from man. Today, milfoil is still present in many areas of the Bay region but it is not the nuisance it once was.

More recently, another exotic species, *Hydrilla verticillata*, has become established in some areas of the Bay. In 1982, hydrilla was first reported in the upper Potomac River. It has since spread to such an extent in the Potomac that a mechanical harvesting program was developed to remove dense mats of the vegetation where they impede commercial or public use of the river.

Major storm events can affect the distribution and abundance of SAV. In 1972, Tropical Storm Agnes caused extensive damage to SAV beds throughout the Bay region. Runoff from heavy rainfall lowered salinities and increased turbidity.

In spite of these periodic or regional fluctuations, Chesapeake Bay SAV has undergone a dramatic decline during the last two decades. This most recent decline of SAV abundance and distribution has affected all species in most areas of the Bay. Currently, the Chesapeake Bay and its tidal tributaries have about 50,000 acres of SAV. This is a fraction of its historic distribution with estimates ranging from 100,000 to 300,000 acres. Since the late 1960s, SAV abundance has dropped by 66%.

Many possible causes for this decline have been proposed including natural population cycles, major weather events, animal grazing and foraging, industrial pollutants and agricultural herbicides. However, it is generally believed by most researchers that this recent loss of SAV is due to a general decline in the water quality of Chesapeake Bay from increased loadings of nutrients and sediment from the surrounding watersheds. Inputs of nutrients are contributed mainly by fertilizers associated with agricultural runoff and by municipal sewage discharges. Major sources of sediments entering the Bay are from agricultural and urban (stormwater) runoff and by eroding shorelines.

The excessive levels of nutrients and sediments entering the Bay inhibit the growth of SAV by increasing the turbidity of the water and limiting the amount of light necessary for the plant to successfully grow and reproduce. Nutrient enriched waters stimulate large algae blooms that can cloud the water.

Summary

There is also an increase in other forms of algae that grow on the SAV leaves and stems further blocking vital sunlight to the plants. Sediments suspended in the water column add to the problem by creating murky water conditions while excessive amounts of sediments can accumulate on the plants.

7.

The overall health and ecological diversity of the Chesapeake Bay has experienced a serious decline in the last two decades. In addition to the loss of SAV, commercially important fish species such as striped bass and American shad have become alarmingly less abundant. Oyster harvests are the lowest recorded in recent history. Canvasbacks, redheads and black ducks, once plentiful waterfowl species in the Bay region, are greatly reduced in numbers. Human population growth and land development have created additional pressures to the Bay system because of increased urban and industrial pollution.

There is, however, a major clean-up effort currently underway by federal, state and local governments and private citizens organizations throughout the Bay watershed. These groups are working together to ensure their programs and management goals seek to restore and protect the Chesapeake Bay and its wealth of natural resources. Because the presence of SAV is directly related to good water quality, it can serve as an indicator of any progress in restoration efforts. Research into restoring SAV through transplanting is being conducted while annual surveys for SAV distribution and abundance around the Bay are taking place.

The *Field Guide to the Submerged Aquatic Vegetation of Chesapeake Bay* covers the more commonly occurring SAV species along with a few non-SAV species that are frequently misidentified as SAV. Species are described by narrative text that presents distinguishing

Chesapeake Bay Submerged Aquatic Vegetation

features of the plant for easy identification. Color photographs are used to depict the plants in their natural state while line drawings are added to show detailed plant structures. An identification key is provided for quick reference and a glossary of relevant botanical terms is included. Additional sources of information on SAV are provided in a list of selected references.

The field guide is intended as a tool for natural resource managers and biologists in the identification of these valuable plants. It is also designed to be an educational aid for all interested individuals who live and work in the Chesapeake Bay watershed.

Common Waterweed

Elodea canadensis
(Family: Hydrocharitacea)

This is sometimes considered an aquatic weed because of its ability to grow rapidly and spread into new regions occasionally clogging water bodies; hence its vernacular name, common waterweed. In the Chesapeake Bay region, however, waterweed is not abundant.

Waterweed has slender branching stems. Leaves are linear to narrowly oval with blunt tips and no leaf stalks. Minute teeth are present along the leaf margins. Leaves are arranged in whorls of three at the stem nodes and become more crowded and overlapping near the stem tips. Waterweed has a weak, thread-like, adventitious root system and can occasionally be found broken free and floating.

Waterweed resembles another SAV, hydrilla, but the latter has prominent teeth on the leaf margins and leaves in whorls of three to five.

Although waterweed is capable of sexual reproduction, reproduction is almost exclusively through vegetative means. Continued growth and branching of the stems and broken stem fragments, produce new plants. Lateral buds are produced along the stem which break off and can remain dormant over winter before developing new plants the following spring.

Waterweed is dioecious with the female

plant being the most prevalent. Male plants are only rarely reported. Because of this, sexual reproduction seldom occurs and seeds are not usually produced. Flowering does occur, however, during the summer. The pistillate and staminate flowers are solitary and enclosed in spathes in the upper leaf axils. The tiny, white flowers grow to the water surface for pollination by elongation of the thin hypanthium or flower stalk. Seeds are slender and smooth surfaced.

Waterweed is a freshwater species and occasionally can be found in slightly brackish waters. It is typically found in the upper reaches of Bay tributaries. Loamy soils and slow-moving waters are ideal for this species. Soils that are too sandy or muddy or strong currents, prevent proper anchorage for water-

9

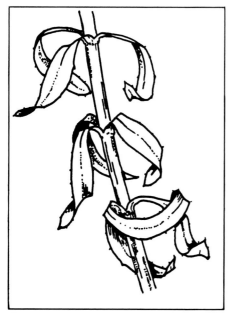

8.

10.

Coontail

weed's slender root system. Waterweed
is associated with waters high in
nitrogen and phosphorus concentrations.

The importance of waterweed for waterfowl food is generally rated as low to
slightly valuable since seeds are rarely
produced. The thick growth of waterweed can provide a habitat for small
aquatic life and because of its associa-
tion with eutrophic waters, it can help
to absorb excess nutrients.

Ceratophyllum demersum
(Family: Ceratophyllaceae)

Coontail, or hornwort as it's sometimes
called, is one of the more common
SAV species. Unlike other species,
it has no true roots. Coontail is found
floating beneath the surface of the water
in dense mats and often floating beneath
or among other SAV. Occasionally,
coontail may be found attached to the
substrate by its basal ends buried in
the sediment. It has slender, densely
branched stems and can attain lengths

13.

14.

up to nine feet. Leaves occur in whorls of nine to ten at each node along the stems. They are divided or forked into linear and flattened segments with fine teeth on one side of the leaf margin. The leaves are stiff and brittle to the touch. The spacing of the whorls of leaves along the stem are variable but generally become crowded and more dense towards the tips of the stem. This gives the plant its resemblance to a racoon's tail and therefore, its common name.

Although coontail is capable of reproducing both vegetatively and by seed, reproduction is predominantly asexual and occurs by fragmentation. The stems of coontail are fragile and easily break apart. Stem fragments that contain lateral buds can develop into new plants throughout the growing season. In autumn, the dense stem tips break off and sink to the substrate where they overwinter, producing new plants the following spring.

Sexual reproduction occasionally occurs in coontail. Coontail is a monoecious plant containing the staminate and pistillate flowers in the leaf axils at separate nodes along the stem. The pistillate flowers occur singularly while the staminate flowers are in pairs. The pollen is released into the water column where it floats into contact with the female flower. A single nut-like seed is produced.

Coontail is found predominantly in the freshwater reaches of Chesapeake Bay tributaries and, because of its fragile nature, slow-moving streams and ponds.

Curly Pondweed

It occurs in waters with moderate to high nutrient concentrations. Because of its rootless nature, coontail is not directly dependent on a particular substrate type and instead, absorbs its nutrients from the water column.

Coontail is a shade tolerant macrophyte, requiring less light than other SAV species for optimum growth. This characteristic combined with its floating ability make turbidity less of a limiting factor for coontail.

The leaves and seeds of coontail are occasionally eaten by waterfowl but its food value is generally reported as slight to fair compared to other SAV species. Because of its ability to form dense mats of vegetation, coontail provides habitat and shelter for fish and small invertebrates.

15.

Potamogeton crispus
(Family: Potamogetonaceae)

Curly pondweed is believed to have been introduced to the United States from Europe during the 1800s. It has a world-wide distribution and today it is common throughout many parts of the country. Although in other areas it can be considered a nusiance plant, in the Chesapeake Bay region its distribution is limited.

The leaves of curly pondweed are broad, linear and finely toothed. They are noticeably undulated or "curly" and arranged alternately or slightly opposite along the flattened, branching stems. The roots and rhizomes are relatively shallow and not as extensive as in other SAV. This perennial plant has different winter and summer forms. The winter plants are blue-green in color and have more flattened leaves, while in summer the plants take on a reddish-brown hue with wider, curlier leaves.

Asexual reproduction occurs through extension of the rhizomes and also through the development of burr-like vegetative structures. These "burrs" usually form near the stem tips. They are spinous and made up of hardened, compact clusters of stipules and leaf bases. These will detach from the plants and remain dormant for many months.

Seed formation occurs during late spring to early summer. The flowers of curly pondweed are borne on short

17.

16.

18.

Eelgrass

spikes extending up to the water surface where pollination takes place.

Curly pondweed has a three-stage life cycle. The vegetative buds may germinate in the fall and the winter form of the plant develops. When spring arrives, the spring/summer foliage appears. Flowering occurs in April to June and the vegetative buds are produced in July. This is followed by a large die-off period and the plants remain dormant until the fall when the vegetative buds germinate and the cycle repeats.

In the Chesapeake Bay area, curly pondweed is apparently limited to freshwater or slightly brackish areas. It is usually associated with silty-clay substrates in moderate to fast-moving waters. Curly pondweed can be frequently found in water with high nutrient concentrations.

It is considered of little importance to waterfowl in the Chesapeake Bay area because of its scarcity, although in other areas the seeds and vegetative parts have been reported as an important food source for waterfowl. As with most SAV, aquatic insects known to be consumed by fish, are found associated with curly pondweed.

Zostera marina
(Family: Zosteraceae)

Eelgrass, unlike other Chesapeake Bay SAV, is a true "seagrass". It is generally restricted to the high salinity regions of the lower Chesapeake Bay and is also found on both the Pacific and Atlantic coasts of North America and along northern Europe coastlines.

Eelgrass has linear, ribbon-like leaves that occur singularly and alternately

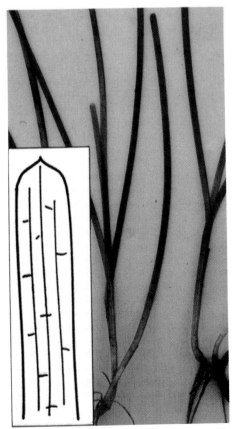

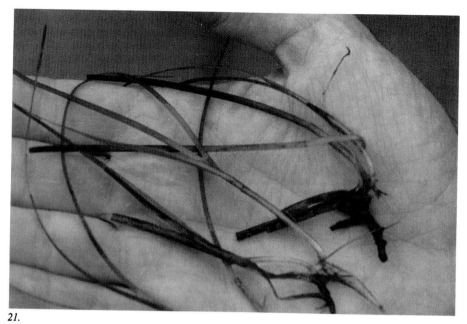

21.

22.

Robert J. Orth

23.

along the joints of the stem which are sheathed by the leaf bases. The tips of the leaves are rounded. Eelgrass has a thick, creeping rhizome with numerous roots.

A similar species, wild celery, can be distinguished from eelgrass by its leaves which arise from clusters at the base of the plant and also by its preference for freshwater habitats.

The length and width of eelgrass leaves can often vary depending upon such factors as water depth and temperature, current, salinity and type of substrate. A short, narrow-leaf form generally occurs in areas where the water is shallow, with high energy (i.e., wave action, strong currents) and sandy substrates. In contrast, a long, wide-leaf form is more common in areas with deeper, less exposed waters and more muddy sediments.

Both sexual and asexual reproduction occur in eelgrass. Asexual reproduction is by growth of the creeping, grass-like rhizomes from which new stems are produced. Flower and seed production take place during spring in Chesapeake

Bay. Eelgrass is monoecious. The male and female flowers are arranged alternately, in two rows, along a spadix or spike, which is enclosed in a long spathe or the sheath-like base of the leaf. Fertilization occurs when thread-like pollen grains drift into contact with the female flowers. The staminate flowers produce pollen before the pistillate flowers on the same plant are fully developed. This prevents self-fertilization from taking place. The plant shoots containing the seeds eventually break off and float to the surface where the seeds are dispersed as the shoots are carried along by the water currents. Seeds can also be dispersed in the surrounding sediments before the shoots are detached. Seed germination takes place during the fall when water temperatures start to decline. The changing photoperiod or daylength may also induce germination.

In Chesapeake Bay, the highest productivity for eelgrass occurs during the spring and fall. In the cold winter months, eelgrass continues to grow, although much more slowly. But, during the summer when water temperatures are high, researchers have suggested that eelgrass becomes heat stressed and its growth markedly declines. This makes eelgrass unique among other Bay grasses which have their highest growth periods during the summer.

Eelgrass mainly occurs in the high salinity waters of the lower Bay and ocean, although it is capable of tolerating salinities in the moderately brackish range. Both eelgrass and widgeon grass can occur in the same areas of the lower Bay, but eelgrass does not seem to do as well as widgeon grass in shallow water.

In Chesapeake Bay, eelgrass grows primarily on sandy substrates. The extensive rhizome growth characteristic of eelgrass gives it the ability to effectively bind and trap sediments thereby stabilizing substrates.

Eelgrass beds have been recognized as an important habitat for both juvenile and adult blue crabs. Other invertebrates and small fish also use eelgrass beds. Eelgrass leaves are used by the bay scallop as a setting substrate.

The decline of eelgrass during the early 1930s from a plant disease had a devastating effect on the population of brant geese *(Branta bernicla hrota)* which depended almost exclusively upon eelgrass as winter food. Being forced to rely on less nutritious foods, such as the algae sea lettuce, many birds perished.

In general, eelgrass has a good food value for waterfowl. The seeds and leaves are primarily eaten and the rootstalks to a lesser extent. Other waterfowl known to use eelgrass for food include black ducks, wigeon, and Canada geese. Redhead ducks in the Chesapeake Bay are attracted to eelgrass beds along the eastern shore of the lower Bay.

Green sea turtles occasionally enter the lower Bay during the summer and consume eelgrass.

Eurasian Watermilfoil

Myriophyllum spicatum
(Family: Haloragaceae)

Eurasian watermilfoil, introduced from
Europe and Asia, presently is found
throughout many parts of the United
States. During the 1960s, this species
went through an explosive growth
period and covered large expanses of
the Chesapeake Bay and its tidal tributaries. For example, it went from
approximately 50,000 acres in 1960 to
100,000 acres in just one year. In some
cases, watermilfoil completely choked
local waterways and marinas creating
difficulties for both commercial and
recreational users of the Bay. By the
early 1970s, however, the watermilfoil
epidemic had ended and the remaining
reduced populations seemed to stabi-
lize. Researchers believe that a virus-
like organism contributed to this
decline along with such other possible
factors as pollution and predation.
Today, watermilfoil commonly occurs
but it does not present the problems it
once did for the Bay region.

Eurasian watermilfoil is distinct from
other Bay SAV. Its characteristic
pinnate or feather-like leaves grow in
whorls of three to four along nodes of
the brownish-green stems. Leaves can
be more abundant near the upper parts
of the stems while numerous, long
roots grow at the lower ends of the
stems anchoring it to the substrate. The
thick, branching stems have an almost
woody-like appearance.

Watermilfoil is monoecious with flowering occurring during late summer.
Spikes of the male and female flowers

24.

25.

28.

26.

27.

where they can remain viable for many years before germinating.

Asexual reproduction takes place mainly by fragmentation. Small broken stem pieces can grow roots and later anchor to become new plants. The upper stems and leaves die-back each fall, but the perennial roots and lower stems over-winter before starting new growth the following spring.

Watermilfoil inhabits fresh to moderately brackish waters. It appears to have an affinity for water with high alkalinity and moderate nutrient loading. In Chesapeake Bay, watermilfoil is commonly found growing on soft mud to sandy-mud substrates in slow-moving streams or protected waters. It is

grow at the stem tips and protrude above the water surface. The upper-most flowers are staminate while the pistillate flowers are at the lower portion of the spike. The tiny, reddish flowers are sessile in the axils of the leaf-like bracts. Pollination takes place aerially. Self-fertilization is prevented by the pistillate flowers maturing before the pollen is produced by the staminate flowers on the same plant. Nut-like fruits are produced which later are released into the water. These will float and eventually sink to the bottom

Horned Pondweed

29.

generally not tolerant of strong tidal currents and wave action.

Watermilfoil is used little by waterfowl as food. The seeds are occasionally consumed by wigeon and other dabbling ducks. Its value to aquatic life is somewhat greater. The finely divided watermilfoil leaves provide numerous substrates for tiny algae and invertebrates. The leaves also are very effective in trapping and holding suspended sediments. Although watermilfoil is not directly consumed by fish, the over-wintering lower stems provide early spring cover for fish fry before other SAV species become established.

Zannichellia palustris
(Family: Zannichelliaceae)

Horned pondweed is a widely distributed species found in many different areas of the Chesapeake Bay. It has also been documented in every state in the continental United States as well as in both Europe and South America. Horned pondweed has long and linear thread-like leaves that are mostly opposite or arranged in whorls along the slender, branching stems. The tips of the leaves have a gradually tapering point while the leaf base is covered by a thin sheath or stipule. Horned pondweed has slender rhizomes with tendril-like roots that anchor the plants in the sediment.

Two similar plants, sago pondweed and widgeon grass, can be confused with horned pondweed when flowers and seeds are not present. Unlike horned pondweed, however, sago pondweed has leaves in bushy clusters while widgeon grass has alternate leaves.

Two growth forms of horned pondweed have been observed in the Chesapeake Bay region. One form consists of upright plants with free-floating branches while a second type has a prostrate or creeping growth form with roots occurring along the stem nodes which anchor it firmly in the sediment. This latter type tends to be found in areas with high wave action.

Reproduction is mostly by seed formation. Horned pondweed derives its name from the distinctive horn-like, occurring together in the same leaf axil. The flowers are not visibly separate, however, since they are both surrounded by a thin sheath. Because the flowers are so close together, horned pondweed may reproduce by self-fertilization. Seed formation occurs very quickly, not long after vegetative growth begins in early spring.

Horned pondweed is usually the first SAV species to occur in spring. But by late June or early July, as water temperatures increase, it rapidly declines. Large mats of decaying plants can be found floating. This serves as a mechanism for seed dispersal. Later, during the fall, when water temperatures cool down, a second growth cycle may occur in some areas of the Bay. Unlike other SAV species, seed germination can take place in horned pondweed during the same year as the seed is set.

Horned pondweed grows in waters that are fresh to moderately brackish and in both muddy and sandy sediments. Because of its two growth forms, it is found in both shallow, low-energy areas and areas with high wave action. The slender leaves and root system make horned pondweed less effective in collecting and holding sediments compared to other more densely foliated species.

Horned pondweed is considered fair to good waterfowl food with both the seeds and vegetative parts being consumed. Large numbers of seeds are eaten by the lesser scaup and shovelers.

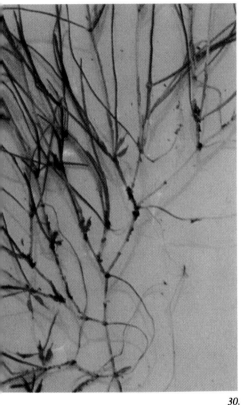

30.

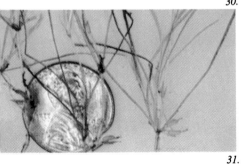

31.

slightly curved fruits that are produced in the leaf axils usually in groups of two to four. It is a monoecious plant with the male and female flowers

Hydrilla

Hydrilla verticillata
(Family: Hydrocharitaceae)

Hydrilla is an exotic species from Southeast Asia that first appeared in the United States during the 1960s, probably via the aquarium trade. It is now found in most southeastern states and as far west as California. Hydrilla was recorded in the Chesapeake Bay region during 1982 in the upper Potomac River near Washington, D.C. It has since spread to such an extent that it covers over 3,000 acres along the

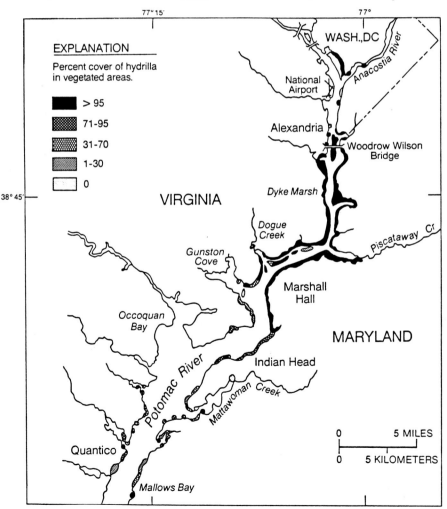

Percent cover of Hydrilla verticillata *in vegetated areas in the tidal Potomac River—1987.*
(From U.S. Geological Survey, Reston, VA)

shallow shorelines of both sides of the river. Hydrilla is also present in the Susquehanna Flats of the upper Bay; however, it is much less abundant and not as widely distributed as in the tidal Potomac River. It is often considered a nuisance aquatic plant because its prolific growth can create dense, practically impenetrable mats of vegetation which impede recreational and commercial use of lakes, rivers, and canal systems. Despite its negative impacts, hydrilla has contributed to an increase in waterfowl and an improve-

ment in the fisheries of the tidal Potomac River.

Hydrilla has freely branching stems with linear to lanceolate leaves in whorls of usually three to five. Leaves have serrated margins and a prominent, spinous midrib giving the plant a brittle, coarse texture when pulled through one's hand. Adventitious roots form along the nodes of the rhizomes that grow horizontally along the top or just below the substrate surface.

Hydrilla can easily be misidentifed as common waterweed. However, the leaves of waterweed are only in whorls of three and are not as markedly toothed.

Hydrilla is capable of reproducing both sexually and asexually. The strain of hydrilla that occurs in the Chesapeake Bay region is monoecious, whereas a dioecious strain occurs elsewhere. The staminate plants of the dioecious strain are rare thus restricting this type to vegetative reproduction. The male and female flowers of the Chesapeake Bay strain occur singularly near the growing tips of the stems. The small, white female flowers are born on a hypanthium at the water's surface. The male flowers detach from the stem and float to the water surface. The pollen is released into the air and must settle directly on the female flower for pollination to take place. Seed set is normally not as effective as vegetative reproduction with success rates of usually less than 50%.

32.

33.

In addition to producing seeds, hydrilla is able to reproduce vegetatively in four different ways. Fragmentation is common in hydrilla. Broken off pieces of stems sink to the substrate and are capable of rooting. A second mechanism of vegetative reproduction is through the lower rhizomes. As the rhizomes grow they can produce new erect stems which grow towards the water surface with developing branches. Two additional vegetative structures of hydrilla are turions and tubers. Turions are resting plant buds that develop in the leaf axils or at the tips of the branching stems. These break off and sink to the substrate, later forming a new plant. Tubers, another type of resting plant bud, develop at the ends of buried runners which branch off the rhizomes.

Both tubers and turions are capable of surviving adverse weather conditions and overwintering. In autumn, as the days become shorter and water temperatures cool, tubers and turions are produced. This is the major form of reproduction in the Chesapeake Bay as cold winter temperatures cause the dense hydrilla beds to die off.

Hydrilla is predominantly a fresh water species. Salinity concentrations of 6 to 9 ppt are at the limit of hydrilla's tolerance, thereby preventing it from dominating large portions of the Chesapeake Bay and its tidal tributaries.

Hydrilla is generally found growing on silt to muddy substrates. It is able to tolerate very low light levels compared to other SAV giving it a distinct com-

34.

35.

petitive advantage. The dense hydrilla beds may reduce the amount of sunlight reaching other slower-growing SAV. Also, its rapid, thick growth can crowd out native SAV.

Hydrilla, like all SAV, provides a habitat for small invertebrates and fishes. Its value to waterfowl is not fully documented, however, mallards, black ducks, Canada geese and coots feed on hydrilla in the Potomac River.

38.

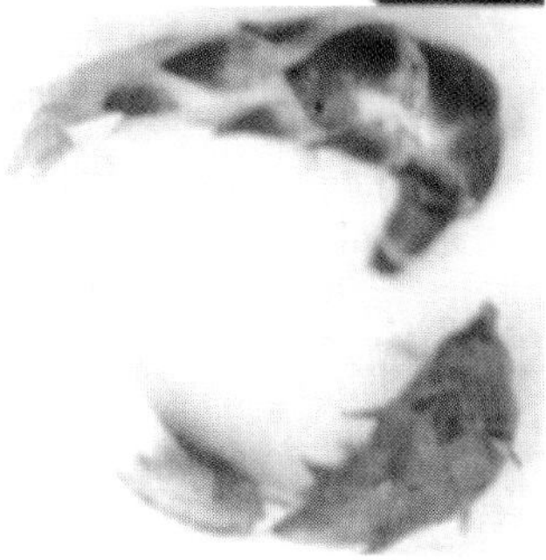

39.

Richard Hammerschlag

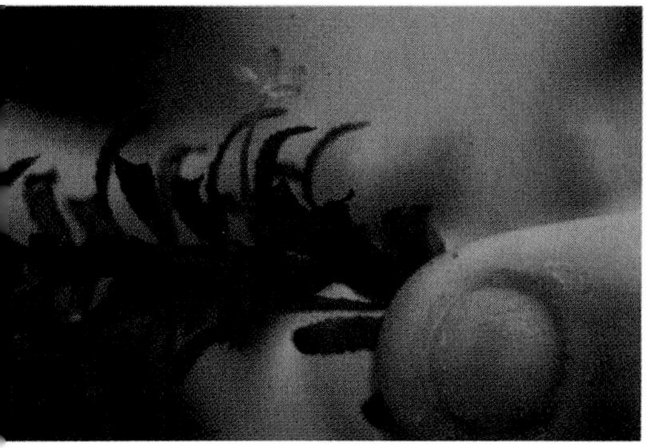

36.

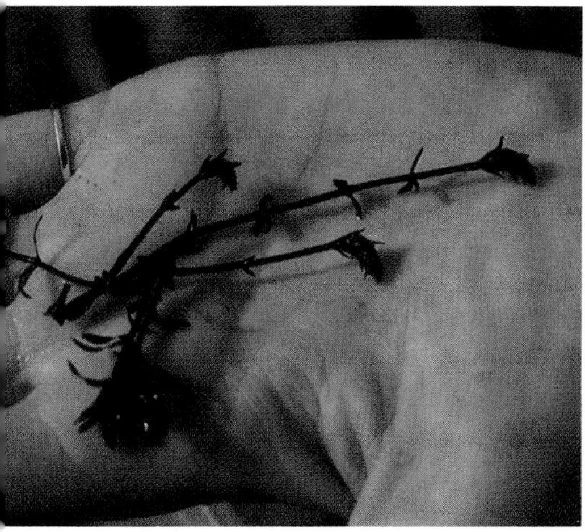

37.

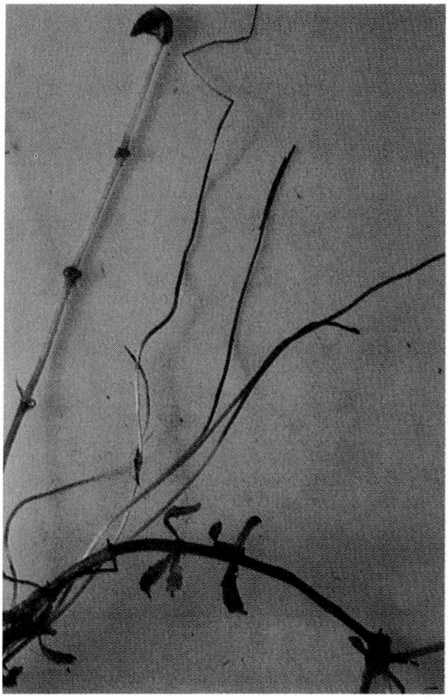

40.

Naiads

Najas spp.
(Family: Najadaceae)

Four species of naiads occur in the Chesapeake Bay region. Southern naiad or bushy pondweed (*Najas guadalupensis*) and *Najas minor* (no common name) are the most common while the northern naiad (*Najas flexilis*) and slender naiad (*Najas gracillima*) occur only rarely. All species are native to the U.S. except for *N. minor* which was introduced from Europe.

The naiads have slender, branching stems. Leaves are narrow, serrated and broadened at the base. They are opposite or in whorls along the stem. The roots of naiads are small and fibrous without rhizomes and tubers.

Reproduction is primarily by seed formation during late summer. Male and female flowers are located in the leaf axils. After the pollen floats into contact with the female flower and fertilization takes place, a single seed develops that will germinate the following spring. The seeds have surface markings characteristic of the species.

42.

41.

43.

All species so closely resemble one another that careful observation with a hand lens is necessary for accurate identification. Key items to look for include the type of toothing along the leaf margins, the shape of the leaf bases and the seed markings. In general, *N. guadalupensis* and *N. flexilis* have wider leaves than the other two species. The bases of their leaves are gradually sloping or rounded near the stem. Leaves are flat and straight in *N. guadalupensis* while in *N. flexilis*

leaves curve out from the stem. The seeds of *N. flexilis* are lustrous and shiny compared to the dull seed of *N. guadalupensis*.

In comparison, the leaves of *N. gracillima* and *N. minor* are much more slender with the sheathing base of the leaf truncated or ending abruptly. *N. minor* can be distinguished from *N. gracillima* by its stiff, recurved leaves and the lengthwise ribs on its seed coat. The teeth on the leaf margins of *N. gracillima* are minute and difficult to see while the marginal teeth of *N. minor* are visible to the naked eye.

The naiads are restricted to small, freshwater streams and the upper por-

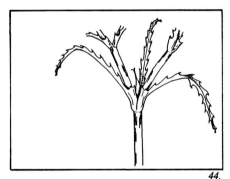

44.

45.

46.

Redhead Grass

Potamogeton perfoliatus
(Family: Potamogetonaceae)

Redhead grass is easily distinguished from other SAV by its flat, oval-shaped leaves, the base of which clasps the plant stems. The leaves are usually arranged alternately to slightly opposite and the leaf margins are slightly crisped. The lower leaves on the stem tend to be oval to lance-shaped. The stems of redhead grass are straight and slender, becoming more branched toward the upper portion of the plant. Redhead grass is securely anchored in the substrate by its extensive root and rhizome system.

47.   48.

tions of Bay tributaries. *N. guadalupensis* also tolerates slightly brackish waters. Although substrates containing a major portion of sand are preferable, the species have been found growing in muddy soils. The naiads are reported to require less light compared to other SAV species.

The value of *N. guadelupensis* and *N. flexilis* as a food source for waterfowl is considered excellent. The stems, leaves and seeds are eaten. Waterfowl known to be fond of these plants are the lesser scaup, mallards and pintails.

N. gracillima, because of its scarcity, is not an important staple for waterfowl while *N. minor* has little nutritional value.

49.

Vegetative reproduction occurs by formation of resting buds at the end of the many rhizomes. These overwinter and grow into new plants the following spring. Sexual reproduction regularly occurs in redhead grass during early to mid-summer. Spikes of tiny flowers emerge from leaf axils on the ends of the plant stems and extend above the water surface. Pollen is released into the air and carried by the wind for fertilization. As the fruits mature, they sink back below the surface and the seeds are later released to the sediments.

Redhead grass is typically found in fresh to moderately brackish and alkaline waters. It seems to grow best on firm muddy soils and in quiet waters

50.

51.

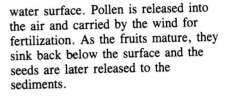

52.

53.

54.

Sago Pondweed

55.

Potamogeton pectinatus
(Family: Potamogetonaceae)

Because of its value to waterfowl, sago pondweed is one of the most important submerged aquatics on the North American continent. It was widely distributed in the United States, and in South America, Europe, Africa and Japan as well.

with slow-moving currents. Because of its wide leaves, redhead grass may be more susceptible to being covered with epiphytic growth than other more narrow-leaved species.

The food value of redhead grass is considered good with the seeds, stems and rootstocks all being consumed. The redhead duck obviously is fond of this particular SAV. Other ducks known to feed on redhead grass include the canvasback, mallard, ring-necked and black duck. Canada geese and tundra swans also relish this valuable food plant. As with all SAV, redhead grass provides a valuable habitat for many aquatic organisms.

56.

Sago pondweed has long, narrow, thread-like leaves that taper to a point. The slender stems are abundantly branched so that the leaves appear in bushy clusters that fan out at the water's surface. The sheathing base of the leaves have a pointed tip or "bayonet" that aids in its identification when not in flower. The slender rhizomes are long and straight.

Two similar plants, horned pondweed and widgeon grass, resemble sago pondweed when without flowers or seeds. Unlike sago pondweed, however, horned pondweed has leaves arranged oppositely or in whorls while widgeon grass has alternate leaves.

Reproduction in sago pondweed is by both seed formation and vegetative reproduction. Sexual reproduction occurs during early summer by forma- tion of a spike of perfect flowers that appear like beads on the slender stalk. Pollen is released from the flowers and floats on the water surface resulting in fertilization. The developing seeds re- main on the rachis of the spike until autumn when they are dispersed in the water. Germination rates are generally

58.

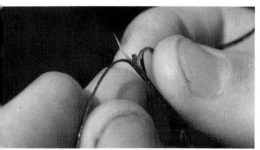

57.

59.

reported as low, making vegetative reproduction more significant.

Vegetative reproduction is by two methods. Starchy tubers are produced at the ends of the underground rhizomes and runners. Another type of tuber can form in the leaf axils at the end of the leaf shoots. These structures occur singularly or in pairs and are

later released and sink to the substrate. After overwintering, both kinds of tubers are capable of forming new plants in the spring.

In the Chesapeake Bay region, sago pondweed is found growing in waters that are fresh to moderately brackish. It is capable of tolerating waters of high alkalinity and seems to be associated with sediments that are of a silt-mud composition. Because its long rhizomes and runners provide a strong anchorage to the substrate, sago pondweed is capable of enduring strong currents and wave action better than most other SAV species.

Sago pondweed's importance to water-fowl cannot be overstated. The highly nutritious seeds and tubers and the tender leaves, stems and rootstocks provide an excellent food for many species of ducks, geese and swans. Marsh and shorebirds as well as muskrats are fond of this palatable plant. Sago pondweed provides a protective habitat for many small fish and invertebrates.

Matthew Perry

60.

Slender Pondweed

Potamogeton pusillus
(Family: Potamogetonaceae)

Slender pondweed, though not very abundant in the Chesapeake Bay region, is, like all pondweeds, an important waterfowl food. It has narrowly, linear, grass-like leaves arranged alternately along slender, branching stems. The leaf blades are entire and have pointed tips. There are usually two small translucent glands at the leaf bases. The bases of the leaves are free from the stipules. Slender pondweed has the root-rhizome system characteristic of most pondweeds.

Smooth-leaved winter buds are formed axillary along the branches and at the terminal ends of stems. These asexual reproductive structures are made up of dense aggregations of leaves that later drop off and overwinter forming new plants in the spring. Flowering and seed development usually occurs in late summer. The flowers are in whorls of three to five along terminal or axillary elongate spikes. After fertilization takes place under water, smooth seeds with rounded backs are produced.

Slender pondweed grows in fresh to slightly brackish waters. Soft, fertile mud substrates and quiet to gently-flowing water seem to be preferred.

Both the seeds and foliage of slender pondweed are eaten by waterfowl. It is considered to have good nutritional value for many species.

61.

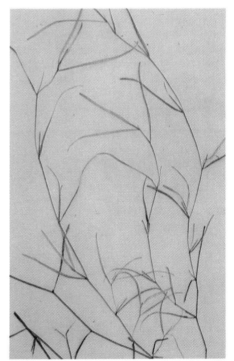

62.

Water Stargrass

Heteranthera dubia
(Family: Pontederiaceae)

Water stargrass, also called mud plantain, has linear, grass-like leaves occurring alternately along freely branching stems. It is firmly rooted in the sediment. There is no distinct midvein on the leaves, while the base of the leaf makes a sheath that wraps around the stem. This species derives its common name from the attractive yellow, star-like flowers that protrude above the water surface during summer.

Unlike other Bay SAV, there is also a terrestrial form of this same species that develops when low water levels occur and the plant is stranded on the substrate, hence the name mud plantain. In this form, flowers are still produced although branching of the stems becomes reduced or absent and the leaves are smaller and leathery.

Reproduction is both by sexual and asexual means. The yellow flowers are perfect, arising from a spathe, with a long thread-like tube divided into six lobes. Flowers that do not reach the surface remain unopened and are self-pollinating. These also produce seeds that overwinter in the sediment until germinating the following spring.

Asexual reproduction occurs throughout the growing season by broken stem fragments that are capable of producing new plants. Over winter, water stargrass becomes dormant and the stems or broken stem tips remain in the sediment until spring.

Water stargrass is found in the fresh-water areas of the Bay and its tributaries. It primarily occurs in slow-moving streams and can also be found in lakes and ponds. Water stargrass is generally found growing in clayey or calcareous soils but it has been reported to grow

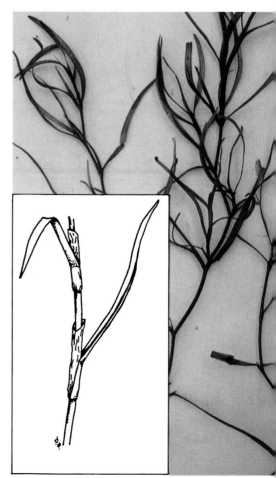

66.

in gravel streams. It is capable of tolerating moderately eutrophic waters.

There are only slight indications of stargrass being used by waterfowl. The seeds and leaves are occasionally consumed for food by a few species of wild ducks such as the pintail and wood duck. The many branching stems and long leaves provide a substrate for algae and small invertebrates.

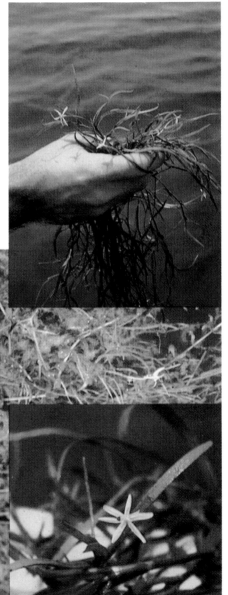

67.

Widgeon Grass

Ruppia maritima
(Family: Ruppiaceae)

Widgeon grass, also known as ditch grass, is one of the more important SAV species because of its importance as food for waterfowl and marsh birds and its ability to tolerate a wide range of salinity regimes. Widgeon grass has linear, thread-like leaves arranged alternately along the slender, branching stems. The sheathing base of the leaf has a rounded tip. Widgeon grass has an extensive root system made up of many branched, creeping rhizomes that lack tubers.

Both vegetative and sexual reproduction occur in widgeon grass. Vegetative

reproduction is through extension of the root-rhizome system from which new stems emerge. Sexual reproduction commonly occurs with flowering usually taking place in late summer. There are two, tiny flowers enclosed together in the sheathing base of the leaves. Widgeon grass has perfect flowers. As the flowers mature, they are extended upward towards the water surface by elongation of a peduncle or flower stalk. The pollen grains are later released from the stamens and float on the surface until making contact with one of the extended pistils. Each fertilized flower produces four oval-shaped fruits that are black with pointed tips. The individual fruits are extended on separate slender stalks with up to eight in a cluster.

When not in flower or with seeds, widgeon grass resembles horned pond-weed and sago pondweed. Unlike widgeon grass, however, horned pond-weed has opposite to whorled leaves and the leaves of sago pondweed are in bushy clusters.

Widgeon grass can be found in a wide variety of habitats because of its ability to tolerate many different salinity con-centrations. It is found in the slightly brackish to moderately brackish waters of the upper and mid-Bay regions and their tributaries. In the lower Bay where salinity levels often approach full strength sea water, widgeon grass along with eelgrass, are the predominant SAV species. They are often found growing together, although widgeon grass is more common in shallow areas and eel-

grass grows in deeper waters. Widgeon grass has even been reported, though very rarely, as growing in the fresh-water portions of some estuaries.

Although widgeon grass can occasionally be found growing on soft, muddy sediments, it is more common on sandy substrates. High wave action can be damaging to the slender stems and

leaves of widgeon grass. Because it is sometimes found growing in shallow ditches containing fertile, organic soil such as tidal marshes, it is also called ditch grass.

Widgeon grass is rated by many as one of the most valuable species of SAV because of its excellent food value for waterfowl. All parts of the plant are

69.

70.

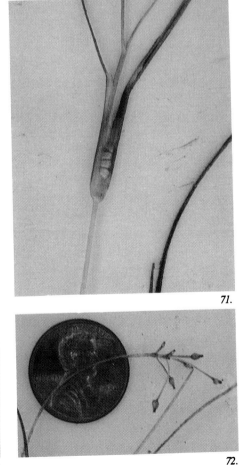

71.

72.

40

eaten. Many species of duck, geese, swans, marsh and shorebirds consume widgeon grass. In some cases, such as for the aptly named wigeon duck, it can contribute up to 25% of the total food intake.

Widgeon grass also provides cover, nursery and spawning areas for fish and invertebrates especially in the high salinity waters where few other SAV species can grow.

73.

74.

75.

Wild Celery

Vallisneria americana
(Family: Hydrocharitaceae

Wild celery, also called tapegrass and sometimes freshwater eelgrass, is not related to the edible garden celery. It is one of our most important SAV species because of its food value for waterfowl. Wild celery mainly occurs in states along the Atlantic Coastal Plain west through Wisconsin and Minnesota, areas that are important for migrating waterfowl.

Wild celery has long, flattened, ribbon-like leaves that arise from clusters at the base of the plant. The leaves are minutely serrulate, with a bluntly rounded tip. A characteristic light green stripe runs down the center of the finely-veined leaves. This is most visible when the leaf is held up in the light. Plants grow from nodes along the creeping underground rhizome from which fibrous roots extend.

Another SAV, eelgrass, can sometimes be confused with wild celery. However, eelgrass has alternately arranged leaves and, because of its preference

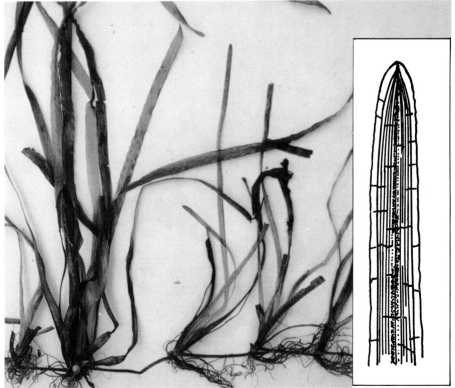

76.   77.

G. Michael Haramis

for high salinity areas, the two species are rarely found in the same location.

Both sexual and asexual reproduction are common. Asexual reproduction is by elongation of the underground rhizomes from which new plants emerge at the ends. Vegetative tuber production commonly takes place. The thick overwintering tubers grow on the ends of underground runners that branch off the rhizomes.

Sexual reproduction regularly occurs in wild celery usually in late July through September. Wild celery is a dioecious plant with both male and female plants frequently found. The numerous staminate flowers are crowded together and enclosed in an ovoid spathe borne

80.

Floating Aquatic Plants

on a short peduncle at the base of the plants. The pistillate flowers occur singularly in a tubular spathe on the end of an exceedingly long peduncle that grows to the water surface from the plant base. The pistillate flowers have three sepals and three white petals. The spathe containing the staminate flowers eventually breaks free and floats to the water surface where the flowers are released and float into contact with the female flowers. Once fertilization is complete, the peduncle of the pistillate flower coils up and draws the developing fruit underwater. A long, cylindrical pod is produced that contains many small, dark seeds.

Wild celery is primarily a freshwater species that occasionally is found in moderately brackish waters. It seems to prefer a coarse silt to slightly sandy soil. Wild celery is fairly tolerant of murky waters and high nutrient loading. It is also better able to tolerate wave action and currents compared to more delicately leaved and rooted SAV species.

Wild celery's food value for waterfowl is excellent with all parts of the plants being consumed. The scientific name of the canvasback, *Aythya valisineria*, aptly demonstrates its affinity for this SAV. Other waterfowl known to feed on wild celery include redheads, lesser scaup, mallards and swans. Non-diving ducks, such as wigeon, have been known to wait on the water surface to feed on plant fragments uprooted by divers. Wild celery also provides habitat for fish and numerous aquatic invertebrates.

Water Chestnut

Trapa natans
(Family: Hygrocaryaceae)

Water chestnut was introduced from Eurasia in the 1800s. It has triangular or diamond-shaped leaves occurring in rosettes that float on the water surface. The upper leaf margins are toothed. The petiole or leaf stalks have swollen portions that aid in flotation. Thread-like submersed leaves are arranged alternately along the lower portions of the leaf stalks. Water chestnut can be free floatly or firmly rooted to the substrate.

This annual plant produces four-petaled white flowers on short stalks among the

44

small leaves. A four-horned, sharply-pointed fruit is produced that can be painful if stepped on. Water chestnut is also known as water caltrop in reference to the spiny fruits. Caltrops were spiked iron balls placed on the ground to delay advancing enemy cavalry and troops.

Water chestnut infested many parts of the eastern United States clogging waterways and out-competing valuable native plants. The use of herbicides and mechanical harvesting were necessary to control its prolific growth. Today, water chestnut is rarely found, although the persistent seed pods are occasionally dislodged from the sediments. Water chestnut is found in fresh to slightly brackish slow-moving waters. It is associated with sediments composed of fine grained muds. Although the seeds are edible, water chestnut is not a duck food plant nor is it known to be eaten by other wildlife.

Duckweeds

Lemna spp., *Spirodela* spp., *Wolffia* spp. (Family: Lemnaceae)

Duckweeds are tiny, free-floating aquatic plants. They are the smallest flowering plants. Duckweeds grow in sheltered freshwater areas. They can create a green blanket covering the water surface which can shade out desirable rooted submerged aquatic plants. Duckweeds are usually found in waters of high nutrient concentrations. They reproduce vegetatively by off-shoots from the floating leaves; flower-

ing occurs less commonly. Duckweeds are considered fair to excellent for waterfowl food depending on the species. Coots, wigeon, wood ducks, and teals are fond of these plants.

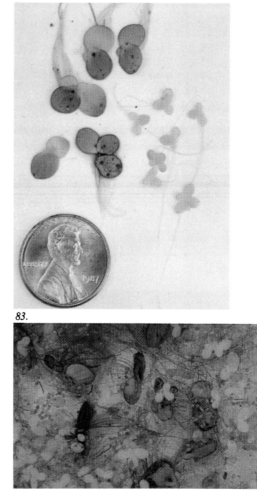
83.

84.

Algae

Muskgrass

Chara spp.

There are over 35 species of this algae and their identification can be difficult. Muskgrasses are often mistaken as a type of SAV, although they have no true leaves, stems or roots. Muskgrass has short, even-length, thread-like branches clustered at joints along the stem-like axis. These usually have clusters of even shorter branchlets. Muskgrass is anchored to the sediment by rhizoids or root-like organs. This algae has a greenish-yellow color and has a brittle feel due to calcium deposits from the water. A skunk-like, musky odor can be detected when crushed, hence the common name.

Another algae, *Nitella* ssp., resembles muskgrass, but it has branches ending in bushy clusters of branchlets and does not have a musky odor.

Sexual reproduction occurs in muskgrasses with reproductive spores being produced at nodes along the branches. Asexual reproduction is by fragmentation of the stem-like axis or by bulbils; a vegetative bud produced at the stem nodes.

Muskgrasses are predominantly found in freshwater with some species occurring in brackish water. They tend to inhabit hard or calcareous waters and are found growing along the bottom of silty or muddy sediments.

Muskgrass is rated as good to excellent in food value for waterfowl. Ducks such as redhead, ring-necked ducks, wigeon, and pintail readily feed on this algae. Coots are also fond of muskgrass.

Sea Lettuce

Ulva lactuca

This larger algae resembles leafs of green lettuce and is commonly referred to as seaweed. It occurs in the brackish to high salinity waters throughout the Chesapeake Bay. Sea lettuce can be found floating or attached to rocks, pilings or the substrate. Following storm events, it is occasionally washed up in large drifts along the shoreline. It can be locally abundant in areas with nutrient enriched waters.

Sea lettuce became a principal food source for brant geese when their primary staple, eelgrass, experienced a

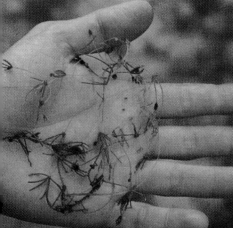

85.

Identification Key to Chesapeake Bay Submerged Aquatic Vegetation

86

massive decline in the 1930s. Canada geese and sea ducks such as scoters and oldsquaw also feed on sea lettuce.

The identification key is not a botanical key in the strict sense, but rather, a non-technical, quick method of species identification. When not in flower or containing seeds, SAV identification can be difficult. For this reason, the key is based on leaf structure and how the leaves are attached and arranged on the stems.

I.   Leaves long, ribbon-like or tape-like
    A. Leaves arise from a cluster at the base of the plant
       Wild celery (*Vallisneria americana*)
    B. Leaves occur singularly and alternately along the stems
       Eelgrass (*Zostera marina*)

II. Leaves feather-like, arranged in whorls along the stems
    Eurasian watermilfoil (*Myriophyllum spicatum*)

III. Leaves forked or divided, arranged in whorls along the stems
    Coontail (*Ceratophyllum demersum*)

IV. Leaves linear and narrow, arranged oppositely or in whorls along the stems
    A. Sheathing bases of leaves are gradually sloping or rounded near the stem
       1. Leaves flat and straight; seeds dull
          Southern naiad (*Najas guadalupensis*)
       2. Leaves curve out from the stem; seeds lustrous and shiny
          Northern naiad (*Najas flexilis*)

B. Sheathing base of leaves
truncated or end abruptly
1. Leaves very stiff and
recurved with teeth visible
to the naked eye
Najas minor
2. Teeth on leaf margins not
visible to naked eye
Slender naiad (*Najas
gracillima*)
V. Leaves linear to lanceolate or slightly
oval; in whorls along the stem
A. Leaves untoothed; in whorls of 3
Common waterweed (*Elodea
canadensis*)
B. Leaves with teeth on margins; in
whorls of 3 to 5
Hydrilla (*Hydrilla verticillata*)
VI. Leaves slender and grass-like;
arranged alternately along the stem
A. Base of leaves wrap around
plant stem
Water stargrass (*Heteranthera
dubia*)
B. Leaves with pointed tips
Slender pondweed
(*Potamogeton pusillus*)
VII. Leaves thread-like
A. Leaves opposite or in whorls
along the stem
Horned pondweed (*Zannichellia
palustris*)
B. Leaves arranged alternately
along the stem
Widgeon grass (*Ruppia
maritima*)
C. Leaves in bushy clusters along
the stem
Sago pondweed (*Potamogeton
pectinatus*)

VIII. Leaves broad; linear or oval-shaped
A. Base of leaves clasp the plant
stem
Redhead grass (*Potamogeton
perfoliatus*)
B. Leaves are finely toothed and
wavy; stems are slightly
flattened
Curly pondweed (*Potamogeton
crispus*)

Glossary

adventitious—developing in an irregular or unusual position especially in reference to buds and roots

alternate leaves—not opposite to each other but at regular intervals along a stem

annual—a plant that completes its life cycle in one year

axil—angle usually formed by a leaf or petiole with the stem

axillary—in or associated with the axis

bract—modified leaf associated with, but not a part of, a flower

dioecious—male and female flowers occurring on separate plants

entire—without teeth or divisions

eutrophic—containing a high concentration of nutrients; particularly nitrogen and phosphorus

fibrous—composed of or resembling fibers

hypanthium—an enlarged or developed flower receptacle

lanceolate—shaped like a lance or arrowhead

lateral—on the sides

linear—long and narrow

monoecious—male and female flowers occurring on the same plant

node—positions on upper stems, usually bearing leaves, or on lower stems, usually bearing roots

opposite leaves—arranged directly across from one another along a stem

ovoid—solid, with an egg-shape

peduncle—flower stalk

perfect flower—having both stamens and pistils

perennial—a plant living more than two years

petals—inner leaves of a flower

petiole—the lower stalk of a leaf

pinnate—leaves arranged on each side of an axis, as in a feather

pistil—seed-bearing organ of a flower

pistillate—containing pistils

pollen—reproductive grains contained in stamens

ppt—parts per thousand

rachis—main axis of a leaf or a group of flowers

rhizoids—slender, root-like organs

rhizome—lower horizontal stems either prostrate on sediment surface or buried; usually with roots and new shoots at stem nodes and curving upward at the ends

rosette—circular cluster of leaves or other structures

runners—branches off buried rhizomes; usually with tubers produced at the ends

sepals—the outer leaves of a flower

serrated—having sharp teeth

serrulate—finely toothed

sessile—without a stalk

sheath—enveloping lower part of leaves

spadix—a spike with a fleshy axis usually enclosed in a spathe

spathe—a large bract enclosing a flower or group of flowers

spike—a group of flowers on an elongated axis

spores—reproductive structure of non-flowering plants

stamen—pollen-bearing organ of a flower

staminate—containing stamens

stipule—appendage at the base of a leaf or its petiole

tendril—a slender, clasping, or twining outgrowth

terminal—at the tips or end

Selected References

truncated—ending abruptly

tubers—vegetative buds (buried in the sediment) usually forming at the end of runners; capable of remaining dormant before developing into new plants

turions—vegetative buds usually formed in the leaf axils or stem tips; capable of remaining dormant before developing into new plants

undulated—having a wavy margin or surface

whorled leaves—arranged in a circle around a stem

Beal, E.O. 1977. A manual of ma. and aquatic vascular plants of Nc h Carolina with habitat data. North Carolina Agricultural Research Service. Raleigh, NC. 298 pp.

Carter, V., P.T. Gammon and N.C. Bartow. 1983. Submersed aquatic plants of the tidal Potomac River. U.S. Geological Survey Bulletin 1543. 58 pp.

Fernald, M.L. 1970. Gray's manual of botany. D. Van Nostrand Company. New York, NY. 1632 pp.

Hotchkiss, N. 1972. Common marsh, underwater and floating-leaved plants of the United States and Canada. Dover Publications, Inc. New York, NY. 124 pp.

Martin, A.C. and F.M. Uhler. 1951. Food of game ducks in the United States and Canada. Research Report 30 (Reprint of USDA Technical Bulletin 634—1939) 308 pp.

Martin, A.C., H.S. Zim and A.L. Nelson. 1951. American wildlife and plants—A guide to wildlife food habits. Dover Publications, Inc. New York, NY. 500 pp.

McAtee, W.L. 1939. Wildfowl food plants—Their value, propagation, and management. Collegiate Press Inc. Ames, IA. 141 pp.

Orth, R.J., A. Frisch, J. Nowak, ar K. Moore. 1989. Distribution of submerged aquatic vegetation in Chesapeake Bay and tributaries 1 Chincoteague Bay—1987. U.S. 'A Final Report. 247 pp.

Reed, Jr., P.B. 1988. 1986 Wet' 1 plant list Northeast region. U' Fish and Wildlife Service. WELUT-86/W13.01. 53 pp

List of Photographs and Plant Drawings

Schloesser, D.W. 1986. A field guide to valuable underwater aquatic plants of the Great Lakes. Extension Bulletin E-1902. Contribution 644. U.S. Fish and Wildlife Service. Ann Arbor, MI. 32 pp.

Stevenson, J.C. (in press). Summary of available information on Chesapeake Bay submerged aquatic vegetation. U.S. Fish and Wildlife Service. Annapolis, MD.

1. Cabot's Quilt—housing insulation made from eelgrass.
2. Bales of eelgrass to be processed into insulation material.
3. Weather station on Mount Washington, NH insulated with Cabot's Quilt.
4. Water chestnut in the Potomac River during the 1930s.
5. Eurasian watermilfoil during the 1960s.
6. Mechanical harvesting of hydrilla on the Potomac River—1988.
7. Epiphytic growth and sediment accumulation on SAV.
8. Leaf structure of common waterweed.
9. Dense mat of common waterweed.
10. Portion of stem of common waterweed.
11. Coontail.
12. Leaf structure of coontail.
13. Coontail with densely, branching stems.
14. Coontail with flowers.
15. Curly pondweed.
16. Curly pondweed with vegetative burr.
17. Curly pondweed with seeds.
18. Curly pondweed with flowers.
19. Eelgrass leaf tip.
20. Eelgrass leaves.
21. Eelgrass.
22. Eelgrass with rhizomes and roots.
23. Eelgrass with seed formation.
24. Eurasian watermilfoil with branching stems.
25. Eurasian watermilfoil leaf structure.
26. Eurasian watermilfoil.
27. Eurasian watermilfoil with flowers protruding from water.

28. Flowers of Eurasian watermilfoil.
29. Sediment accumulation on Eurasian watermilfoil.
30. Horned pondweed with branching stems; seeds present.
31. Seeds of horned pondweed.
32. Dense hydrilla beds on Potomac River.
33. Hydrilla.
34. Hydrilla with branching stems.
35. Leaf structure of hydrilla.
36. Hydrilla with flower.
37. Hydrilla with tuber formation.
38. Hydrilla with flower.
39. Hydrilla tuber (above) and turion (below).
40. Hydrilla with adventitious roots.
41. Southern naiad with seed (above) and flower (below) in leaf axils.
42. Southern naiad.
43. Southern naiad with seeds in leaf axil.
44. Leaf structure of *Najas minor*.
45. *Najas minor*.
46. Branching stems of *Najas minor*.
47. *Najas flexilis*
48. *Najas gracillima*.
49. Redhead grass with flowers.
50. Redhead grass.
51. Leaf structure of redhead grass.
52. Seeds of redhead grass.
53. Flowers of redhead grass.
54. Flowers of redhead grass.
55. Flowers of redhead grass.
56. Sago pondweed with flowers and seeds.
57. "Bayonet" of sago pondweed.
58. Sago pondweed flowers.
59. Seeds of sago pondweed.
60. Sago pondweed tubers.
    (top) tubers digested by waterfowl
    (bottom) undigested tubers.
61. Slender pondweed.
62. Slender pondweed with branching stems.
63. Leaf structure of water stargrass.
64. Water stargrass with branching stems.
65. Water stargrass with flowers protruding from water.
66. Flowers of water stargrass.
67. Water stargrass flower.
68. Widgeon grass.
69. Seeds of widgeon grass.
70. Seeds of widgeon grass.
71. Flowers of widgeon grass enclosed in sheathing base of leaf.
72. Seeds of widgeon grass.
73. Maturing widgeon grass flowers on elongating flower stalk.
74. Flowers and peduncle of widgeon grass.
75. Dense widgeon grass bed.
76. Wild celery plants with rhizome and roots.
77. Leaf structure of wild celery.
78. Dense bed of wild celery.
79. Wild celery tubers.
80. Staminate flowers of wild celery.
81. Pistillate flowers of wild celery.
82. Water chestnut with flowers and spiked fruits.
83. Duckweeds.
84. Duckweeds.
85. Muskgrass.
86. Sea lettuce.

TAKE
PRIDE IN
AMERICA